PADDO

PHIL KETTLE & BOB ANDERSEN

Illustrated by Shane McGowan

Wellington

First published in Australia in 2022 by
Wellington (Aust) Pty Ltd
(ACN062 365 413)
433 Wellington Street
Clifton Hill, Vic. 3068
Australia

A catalogue record for this
book is available from the
National Library of Australia

Paddock Bomb
ISBN: 978-1-925308-84-6 (print)
       978-1-925308-83-9 (ebook)

Designed by Workingtype Pty Ltd
Printed in Australia by IngramSpark

Contents

Welcome to
the Outback

Three months ago, my life changed in a way that I never dreamed possible.

It was a Friday and it was the thirteenth day of the month, which is supposed to be unlucky for some. And that Friday was definitely unlucky for my Uncle Buck.

Uncle Buck owned a HUGE sheep station way out woop-woop, and he had been mustering sheep all day when a wild storm struck. Sadly for Uncle Buck, he was hit by lightning and sizzled like a sausage on a very hot barbecue.

When we received the news, Mum and Dad were VERY, VERY sad, but that all changed a few weeks later when we got an unexpected call from Uncle Buck's lawyer. It turned out that Uncle Buck had left his sheep station to my family in his will. Mum's and Dad's tears turned to smiles – suddenly we owned a sheep station in outback Australia!

Two days later, we had a family meeting to decide what we were going to do. It was decided by two votes to one that we were leaving our city home and moving to the outback. (You can probably guess who was the 'one'.)

Faster than I could wave goodbye to my city friends, Mum and Dad packed up and headed off to Overflow Station, dragging me along with them.

My name is Clancy, I'm eleven years old and these are the stories of my outback adventures.

Meet the Gang

That's me, Clancy!

That's my mum...

and that's my dad.

This is Brutus, my pampered city pooch.

Big Bill is the manager
at Overflow Station...

And Little Bill
is his daughter!

And that's Butters,
Little Bill's farm dog.

Chapter 1

Get It Off the Road!

Dad was grumpy. He'd just been into town in the car we brought with us when we moved from the city to the Overflow Station. It wasn't really suited to country roads. Anyway, when he was in town the local cop pulled him over and said he had to

'Get it off the road!!' When Dad argued with him the cop said Dad was a menace to all the people in Chance and if he let Dad drive around the streets, he was likely to have a serious accident on his hands.

'And another thing,' said the cop, 'if you weren't related to Uncle Buck I'd be giving you a ticket!'

I guess the cop missed Uncle Buck. Everyone knew Uncle Buck in Chance.

'What are we going to do?' Mum asked.

'Well,' said Dad, 'the town car isn't very useful out here. We need something that can carry the kids and a bale of hay or a sheep or two. I think the fence posts I bought the other day put the kibosh on the town car. Seems to have ruined the suspension. Every time you go over a bump on the track or even on the road there's a horrible scraping noise.'

'And you can't sit on the back seat anymore,' said Mum, 'because it's covered in dog hair. When Clancy got out to go to the supermarket the other day, I thought he'd grown a tail. If anything happens to Brutus and we have to get another dog, don't get a shedder!'

Dad made a big decision. 'I'll go and see the bank manager next time I'm in town, and if he won't lend me the money, I'll get a loan through the car dealer. I think the bank interest rate will be cheaper, but you never know. The big question is, what sort of car should we buy?'

'If we're going to keep you out of gaol, then we'd better do something,' said Mum. 'Do you think we could trade in the old car – we should get something for it?'

'I'll see what the car dealer says,' said Dad. 'We should get something for it.'

Dad often repeats what Mum says. It seems to give him time to think about what she's saying, but it drives me crazy. Mum's so used to it now she doesn't say anything.

Mum made a cup of tea and they sat

down to discuss what sort of new car they needed. It wasn't long before they decided on a four-door ute with four-wheel drive. 'That would be perfect!' said Dad, who had wanted a ute for years. 'And because it's a dual cab,' he said, we can use it for family outings as well.' Mum agreed for once but she did suggest that Dad should ask Big Bill whether an automatic or gear shift would be better.

'I think I'm old and wise enough to know what sort of gear box I need without wasting Big Bill's time,' said Dad.

Mum rolled her eyes.

Chapter 2

Buying a new car

'You can come with us, Clancy.' It was the next day and Dad was focused on the new ute. He had an appointment with Mel Bell, the car dealer in Chance.

'We'll need all the help we can get,' he said, passing me a hand-written list of colours. For a moment I wondered what it all meant, but then I realised it was Mum's handwriting and these were her preferred colours. I'd heard her say, 'Not black! It shows all the dirt. And the same with white.' She seemed pretty keen on green, or even red, but her favourite was silver.

I suggested to Dad that we should go for silver.

'Good idea,' said Dad and we were soon

on our way. We stopped at Little Bill's house and picked her up and her dog Butters. Butters took up a lot of the back seat so it was a good thing we didn't have Brutus as well. Anyway, Brutus makes Butters very edgy and that drives Dad mad. Even with only Butters, Little Bill and me in the back the underneath of the car dragged on the ground whenever we went over a bump or the ruts in the road got too deep.

Halfway there it started to rain. Dad had to stop because he couldn't see out the front window. 'I should have replaced the windscreen wipers,' he said, 'but it's too late now. The new owner will have to do that.'

Little Bill snorted. 'Who'd want this useless old heap of...' Fortunately she didn't finish the sentence. Dad really loved his car.

'A car reflects your personality,' he told Little Bill. 'This useless old heap, to use your term, was the car in which I courted

Clancy's Mum. I proposed sitting where I am now and Clancy's Mum was sitting where she is now, beside me. It was a romantic time for us both.'

We had to stop a few times along the road to Chance. Every time it rained Dad had to pull over. At one stage we had to stop to let Butters out for a pee – that's how long it took to get there! Also, Dad drives at about 30 ks an hour.

'Does he always drive like this?' Little Bill hissed at me. 'We'll never get there at this rate. Tell him to get on with it.'

'Come on, Dad,' I said, 'put your foot down!' But Dad muttered something under his breath which sounded like 'I wish we hadn't brought those kids along. They're driving me crazy.' But I know he loves us.

When we got to Chance we didn't have any trouble finding the car dealer. There were flags and cars and utes and even a

Winnebago. When I grow up I'm going to travel around Australia in a Winnebago. I am thinking of asking Little Bill whether she'd want to come too. I suggested this to Little Bill.

'I think a Winnebago might be a bit much for you to handle,' said Little Bill. 'May be a pop-top would be more your style.' I hoped she was joking.

There were caravans and pop-tops and a whole section for tractors and farm equipment

Mel Bell, the car dealer, was also easy to find. He was a big man and he was wearing a tie. It had pictures of palm trees and tropical fruits on it. I don't think we've seen someone with a tie on since we left the city for the Overflow, but big old men wearing ties seems to be the go when you're buying a new car. 'It would be good if we could talk to a woman,' said Little

Bill to Mum. They know more about these things!'

'And they don't wear ties that are thirty years old,' said Mum.

Mel ignored Mum and Little Bill and me. He showed Dad a twin-cab ute and Dad was blown away. It was silver and had a 'big six', according to Mel, and would be the perfect vehicle for the farm.

'How does he know?' Little Bill whispered to me. 'He's never even seen your farm.'

Mum was looking daggers at Mel but he didn't seem to notice. 'You'll want a test drive then,' he said to Dad, and Little Bill and I were really excited. We had never had a ride in a twin cab before. 'But that mutt isn't coming,' said Mel, pointing at Butters.

Little Bill muttered something that caused Mel to cock his ear and say, 'What was that? in a stern tone, so she buttoned her lip and we both waited on the footpath.

'There's no way I'm not coming!' announced Mum and she grabbed the back door handle and scrambled in before Mel could take off with Dad.

When they came back the windows in the cab were down and we heard Mum saying, 'That's outrageous!' in a very loud voice. 'Take it or leave it,' said Mel to Dad, ignoring her again.

'Well, I want to take it,' said Dad, 'but you're making it very difficult for me. With

interest rates like that I'll end up paying for the ute twice!'

'Then you'd better go and see Brian down at the bank,' said Mel. 'He might be able to do a better deal for you.'

So we all walked across the road to the bank. On the way Mum told us that 'that crook' wouldn't even take the old car off their hands, let alone give them something for it. 'He said it would cost him $500 dollars to dispose of it,' said Dad indignantly. 'Dispose of it!' Dad was not happy. 'This car has served me well for twenty years and it has a lot more life in it yet.'

Chapter 3

Getting the Money

Brian, the bank manager, also wore a tie but his was covered in sheep. It was meant to make you feel he was a country boy at heart. 'How can I help?' he said, getting down to business straight away. You could tell he was a townie – he didn't have time for a chat. Also, he was talking to Mum as well as Dad.

Dad explained how they needed a new car and wanted to get a loan. 'I can do that now,' said Brian and so Dad gave us a few bucks and Little Bill and I went off for ice cream down the road. Brian looked relieved when we took Butters with us. We tied Butters up to the horse rail outside the milk bar and went inside for the ice creams.

We were there looking at all the things we could have when Mum and Dad came through the door, saying, 'All done'.

'We'd better get back and see Mel,' Dad said.

'Boy, that didn't take long,' said Little Bill. 'That's the city for you,' said Dad proudly, 'instant service!'

Little Bill looked up at the ceiling. I'm

glad she didn't say anything, because Dad was on a roll. And even Mum looked happier.

On the walk over to the car dealership Dad said, 'I'll take you guys home and Mel will bring the new ute out this arvo, and then I'll drive him back into town. How does that sound? That way we won't have to hang around for the paperwork, so he can do that and bring it with him.'

'As long as you don't let him leave until I've had a very good look at the paperwork,' said Mum firmly.

'Why can't we leave the old car here and drive the new ute home?' I asked, thinking how much quicker that would be, especially since it was looking like rain again.

'Because Mel won't take the old car off my hands, so we can just use it around the farm,' Dad said.

'You can use it as a paddock bomb,' said

Little Bill. 'Everyone should have one. It's the best way to learn to drive when you're our age.'

I remembered my first effort at driving and how we crashed into that tree. I hadn't tried to drive a car since then. It was kind of Little Bill not to mention that incident, but perhaps she'd forgotten it! There'd been a lot of water under the bridge since then.

'I'm not sure about that, Little Bill,' said Mum. 'Isn't it illegal?' Mum had obviously remembered the last incident but wanted to avoid mentioning it.

Little Bill went on, unfazed, 'No worries, Clancy's mum. Who's going to see you on the farm? Anyway, it would be good for Clancy. He can drive to the gate to get the school bus.'

'All right, all right,' said Dad, 'we'll think about it.' But if Little Bill suggests something I know Mum and Dad pretty much always accept her view.

That afternoon Mel Bell arrived in the new ute. We were all on the front verandah, and beside Dad's old car the new ute looked huge.

'Chalk and cheese,' Dad said in a dreamy voice. He was already in love with his new ute.

'What about the car you proposed to Clancy's Mum in?' asked Little Bill. 'Have you forgotten about that already?'

'Well, that was a while ago now,' said Dad, 'and I did choose Mum's favourite colour for the ute. I see it as a bit of a remembrance thing.'

Mum rolled her eyes again but Mel wanted to get back to the subject in hand. I think he sensed a confrontation coming on and he didn't want to lose the sale. He changed the subject.

'Good thing you wanted silver because

it was the only one I had in stock,' he said, waving the paperwork in one huge hand.

'Come on inside and we'll sign it,' said Dad, 'and I can drive you back to Chance. Dear, can you put on a cup of tea for Mel?'

Mum was having none of it. 'I think it's important that I check the paperwork as well,' she said, taking the papers out of Mel's outstretched hand. 'You put the kettle on, Francis.'

I could see that things were hotting up.

'Sure thing, Clancy's Mum, best if you look through things. I can sometimes get the details wrong,' said Mel and the three of them went inside.

Little Bill and I sat on the verandah and I admired the new ute. Little Bill was more interested in Dad's old car. 'It'll be perfect for a paddock bomb,' she said. 'We could paint it a new colour.'

I was just thinking about whether

purple would look good when Mel and Dad came quickly out the door.

'All right, all right!! Whatever you say!' Mel was saying loudly to Mum, who was still back in the house.

I heard Mum call back, 'Then it's agreed!'

Mel and Dad climbed up into the ute and headed off to Chance. I'm not sure if Mel slammed the door closed on purpose or it was just a mistake.

Chapter 4
The Driving Lesson

The next day I asked Mum and Dad whether I could try and drive the old car, which Little Bill now called Clancy's paddock bomb. Dad was reluctant at first but he was so excited with his new ute that he didn't really object.

Then Little Bill turned up with Butters and she said she'd teach me to drive. 'You've got to forget about that first effort,' she said. 'Pretend it never happened. And anyway, you were a city slicker then and now you're nearly a country boy.'

Was she serious? I think it's the first time she's had something good to say about me!

Anyway, Little Bill knows how to do everything and so I said, 'Let's go,' and we piled into the old car.

Butters seemed strangely reluctant. He sat there looking very uncertain. Then he started whining. 'Get over it, Butters!' said Little Bill, but she had to get out and push him into the back seat.

Little Bill explained the brake, the clutch and the accelerator to me. It all seem pretty simple really. The gear stick was more

difficult. It was a 'four on the floor' she explained, whatever that meant, and we sat there while I pushed down the clutch pedal and changed from first gear to second gear and so on about a hundred times. Reverse was really hard because you had to lift the stick and then give it a bit of a twist.

She explained how you need some acceleration or the car will stall. That meant putting my foot on the accelerator. The engine roared. There was nothing wrong with the engine – just the suspension – but I was having trouble reaching the pedals.

'I think you're too short to reach the pedals,' Little Bill said, 'but I know the answer. I've got my old baby booster seat from when I was a baby. I'll get that and you can put it on the driver's seat.'

She set off to her place while I practised my work on the clutch and changing gear. Butters went with her. He seemed glad to get out of the car.

When Little Bill came back with the booster seat I was very confident. I was up so high that my head nearly touched the roof of the car She struggled getting Butters into the car again but we put on our safety belts, fired up the motor and I set off. The booster seat allowed me to see out the front window, but reaching the pedals was still a bit hard.

After a jumpy start we set off down the track to the main road.

'You're not allowed to go on the road,' Little Bill said, 'so you'd better head off across the paddock.' She pointed off to my right and it seemed flat enough. I was quite relaxed as everything seemed to be going OK. I started thinking about a career as a Formula One racing driver. Or even Mount Panorama... Here comes Clancy driving his modified paddock bomb.

Chapter 5

The accident

I'm not sure what happened next. I think the car hit a dip or bump and, seeing as how the suspension was a bit dodgy, the car heaved to the right and I was thrown off the booster seat. My foot pressed down on the accelerator and I couldn't shift it. Little Bill pulled on the hand brake but that didn't do any good. Butters started barking and whining in the back seat. It was very confusing.

'Take your foot off the accelerator!' yelled Little Bill, but I couldn't do a thing. The booster seat had jammed my right leg down and I couldn't reach the brake with my left leg. We started heading towards some trees but Little Bill grabbed the steering wheel and the car slewed round and headed off in the other direction.

We rocketed across the paddock – down into hollows and up again. Little Bill held on to the wheel and if something looked dangerous she'd pull at it so that the car headed of in another direction. We seemed to be going faster all the time.

'Switch off the engine!' yelled Little Bill but I couldn't reach the key. There was a loud crunch and the sound of tearing metal as we lost the exhaust system. The engine noise sounded like a jumbo jet on take-off. Butters was screaming in the back seat.

At this stage we came over a small hill and a flock of startled sheep were directly in front of us.' The horn, the horn!' shouted Little Bill, but I didn't know where the horn was. Anyway, I was more concerned with trying to get my foot off the accelerator. The sheep ran in all directions and we

raced through, only just avoiding the water trough and heading for the dam.

Butters must have seen the dam ahead because his whining began again. It was a high-pitched scream and you could even hear it over the sound of the engine, which was at least a thousand decibels. 'Can you shut the dog up?' I screamed at Little Bill. I must have been losing my cool.

At that stage I was hoping Little Bill might pull on the wheel so that we missed the dam, but we were going so fast that if we had tried to turn the car we would have rolled it over.

'We'll drive into the dam,' shouted Little Bill. 'That will stop us!'

We drove up the slope of the dam wall at high speed. I was trying to remember whether there was water in the dam. I hoped not. I didn't want to drown. A flock of pelicans took flight. A startled shag raced away from the speeding car and then we were over and the car went a few yards into the dam. Fortunately it was nearly empty and the car sank into the mud. The engine spluttered and stopped. Little Bill and Butters got out of the car and came round to help me out. They were in mud up to their knees.

Chapter 6

Mel Bell

We trudged back to the house. We were covered in mud. Dad was still mucking about with the new ute. He stared at us like he was in shock. 'What's happened? Are you OK?'

'The car's stuck in the dam near the main road,' said Little Bill. 'Clancy nearly killed us all!'

'It was your stupid booster seat that caused the problem!' I said. I wasn't going to be blamed for the accident if I could help it.

Little Bill described the episode to Dad. I could see that he was about to lose his temper and tell us both off for being stupid, but then he must have thought better of it. After all, he hadn't stopped us when Little Bill first suggested the driving lesson.

'You'd better go and let Mum know,' he said sheepishly.

If I tell her she'll let me have an earful.'

'It could be a good opportunity to try out the new ute,' said Little Bill craftily. Dad leapt at the idea. 'I can see if it will pull the car out of the dam! It should be better than the tractor if Mel is right about its pulling ability with the tow bar. Little Bill looked at me and I knew what she was thinking. What if Mel was wrong and the new ute couldn't budge the car. After all, it was pretty thoroughly bogged.

'And another thing,' said Dad, 'you're not getting into the new ute covered in mud like that and that dog is certainly not getting in.'

'Can we ride in the back?' asked Little Bill.

'Only if you wash that mud off first,' said Dad.

'But we'll be covered in mud again when we get into the dam to push the paddock bomb,' Little Bill said. Dad reluctantly agreed but you could see he was too excited about trying out the new ute to worry too much.

So in the end we all piled in the back of the ute – Butters, a good strong towing rope from the shed and a few planks of 4 x 4 to use as levers – and we were off. You've got to give it to Uncle Buck, his shed had everything you'd ever need on a farm.

'Do you think your dad's up to this?' whispered Little Bill. 'Perhaps we should have asked my dad to come and help.'

'I think it's important for Dad to do something useful,' I explained to Little Bill. 'He's been a bit lost lately, what with Mum and Big Bill doing all the heavy lifting.'

'I think he's doing well,' said Little Bill. 'What about that chookshed he built?'

Dad drove very carefully. He didn't want to damage his new truck and I think Little Bill and Butters were pretty happy about that. I certainly was. Dad followed the path the car had made through the grass. You could see where we'd swerved to miss the water trough. We also found the muffler and the exhaust system in the middle of the paddock, and we stopped and threw them into the back of the ute. Eventually we made it to the dam.

Chapter 7

Covered in Mud

As we came over the lip of the dam a very sorry site was revealed. The car had sunk even further into the mud. We couldn't have opened the doors if we'd been inside now.

'I don't think the ute is going to do it,' said Dad, 'even with the big six and the special industrial tyres. We'll give it a go, but I might need Big Bill's help as well. See how you go with those levers.'

Little Bill and I put one 4x4 plank on each side of the car while Dad tied the tow rope to the tow bar on the car and ran it up to the ute. The ute had special towing gear on the back and Dad fastened the rope to it.

'We'll need a spade to dig under the car

and then we'll need something to put the levers on,' said Little Bill. She was right and we weren't helped by being up to our knees in mud.

'Make sure you don't get bitten by a yabbie,' yelled Little Bill. 'They live deep down in the mud this time of year.'

All of a sudden I thought I felt something crawling around under my feet!

We started digging and it was hard work. The sheep had got over their earlier fright and had come back down to the dam to see what was going on. They peered over the edge of the dam and when they saw Butters they jumped away again. A good thing Brutus wasn't with us as he would have driven us crazy chasing the sheep. That's why we didn't take him with us when we worked around the farm.

We found a couple of rocks to help with the levers. The idea was that we would try and lever the car up while the tow began,

but everything kept sinking into the mud and we weren't much help. Nevertheless Dad revved up the ute while Little Bill and I tried to lift the car out of the mud. There was a lot of noise but nothing moved. The mud was up to our knees and the feeling of it between my toes was awesome.

'I love the feeling of mud between my toes,' I said to Little Bill, but she shrugged and said, 'I still reckon our toes are in some yabby holes. If you feel something biting you get your foot out pronto. Yabbies can do a lot of damage, you know.' I guessed she was kidding.

It was then that Big Bill arrived with the tractor. I think Mum must have told him where we were, which is strange because I didn't think she knew about the paddock bomb.

'You'll never budge it,' he said to Dad and so we changed the tow rope from the ute to the tractor and hey presto, the car came out. It made a huge sucking noise and there was water in the hole it left behind. The sheep were looking on again and I think I heard them cheer, or perhaps I was fantasising.

Dad and Bill tried to start the car, but it wouldn't start. I was quite relieved. I'd had enough driving lessons for one day. I don't think Little Bill wanted to teach me anything else either.

'I'll tow it back to the farmhouse,' said Big Bill, and off he went.

Little Bill, Butters and I climbed into the back of the ute. We were knackered and covered in mud. 'Time to go home,' said Little Bill, and even Butters looked happy.

'I'm not sure about learning to drive,' I said to Little Bill. 'Perhaps a horse is more my style.' I sat there thinking that maybe instead of being a formula one driver I could be a rodeo rider. Was that too silly? I won't mention it to Little Bill in case she's got other ideas.

When we got to the main house Mum was in the vegie garden watering her plants. 'Come over here, you two,' she said and she turned the hose on both of us.

'I don't want you walking mud into my house or getting anywhere near the new ute!' She seemed quite upset.

'I think it's because the proposal car is looking a big mess,' whispered Little Bill,

although I wasn't sure if that is what she said because the hose water was freezing and we were both jumping around trying to stay away from the spray.

Eventually we were pretty clean and Mum went inside so Little Bill and I borrowed the hose and started washing down the paddock bomb.

'We'll need to get the mud off it before we can paint it,' said Little Bill.

I opened the driver's door to have a look inside and maybe even get rid of the booster seat, and guess what? There was a pool of muddy water on the floor and in it were three yabbies.

'Hey, Little Bill,' I yelled, 'get a bucket!'

Outback Facts:
Car Acronyms

ABS: Antilock Braking System – prevents the wheels from locking during emergency braking.

AWD: All-Wheel Drive – power is fed to all four wheels, otherwise known as four-wheel drive or 4WD.

BHP: Brake Horsepower – brake horsepower is the horsepower of an engine measured by the degree of resistance offered by a brake, which represents the useful power that the machine can develop.

DDI: Direct Diesel Injection – atomised

diesel fuel is sprayed directly into the combustion chamber of each cylinder, improving performance and fuel economy.

DFI: Direct Fuel Injection – fuel is injected directly into the engine instead of mixing it with air before it reaches the intake valve passage.

DRL: Daytime Running Lights or Daytime Running Lamps – low-energy lights that switch on automatically whenever the vehicle is in operation to increase the visibility of the vehicle to other road users.

DSG: Direct-Shift Gearbox – a dual-clutch gearbox which allows either full automatic operation or semi-manual control via the floor-mounted gear selector and steering-wheel paddles.

EV: Electric Vehicle – any type of vehicle that is primarily powered by an electric motor. Can include Extended-Range Electric Vehicles (E-REVs), Plug-in Hybrids (PHEVs) and Hydrogen Fuel Cell (HFC) vehicles.

FWD: Front-Wheel Drive – engine power and torque is channelled to the front wheels only.

GPS: Global Positioning System – the network of satellites that provides the location and time information used by a vehicle's Satellite Navigation ('Sat Nav') system.

Outback Jokes

Q. What do you need to be able to drive in the Outback?

A. You need to show koala-fications.

Q. What's got four wheels and flies?

A. A garbage truck.

Q. Why can't cars play football?

A. Because they only have one boot

Q. What do you get when dinosaurs crash their cars?

A. Tyrranosauros wrecks.

Q. What do you say to a frog that needs a ride?

A. Hop in.

Q. Which part of the car is the laziest?
A. The wheels because they are always tired.

Q. Where do Volkswagens go when they get old?
A. The old Volks' home.

Q. What kind of a car does an egg drive?
A. A Yolkswagen

Q. What sound does a witch's car make?
A. Broom broom!

Q. What cars do snakes drive?
A. Ana-honda

Q. Where do dogs park their cars?
A. In the barking lot.

Outback Poem

The Paddock Bomb

Phil Kettle & Bob Anderson

My paddock bomb's my favourite car.
It's travelled near and travelled far.
It's old and rusty, scratched and dinged –
Who cares – it's still my favourite thing!

If you are an outback person
A paddock bomb is almost certain
To bring you joy, though sometimes scary,
And narrow misses can be hairy!

Because these cars are barely legal
And country cops have eyes like eagles,
The paddock's where they need to stay
If you don't want them towed away.

They all have dents and dirt and scratches,
No springs, flat tyres and rusty patches,
But still I say, without a doubt,
A paddock bomb will sort you out!

Other Titles in this Series

Here are some more of my adventures ...

City Slicker

It was a bit of a shock to move from the city to Overflow Station, but I thought I could handle it. And then I met Little Bill, and she was a great big shock! I couldn't help feeling I'd never learn how to handle her. I do know that I was involved in a major accident, thanks to Little Bill, and I survived!

Chookshed Blues

I thought that buying a few chickens would be easy, but then Dad got involved, and I think you'll guess the rest. But I had a lot of fun helping with the chooks, and I'm starting to have some fun on the Overflow, though Little Bill never stops telling me what to do!

Shearing Time

I was really excited thinking about sheep shearing, even if it was Little Bill who had to explain everything to me. The shearers were a lot of fun, but they have a thing about food. It's a good thing they don't live in the city. I can just see them pulling the capsicum off the pizza before eating it!

Road Kill Rescue

The bad news is that the school bus killed a kangaroo. The good news is that her joey survived. I've learned a lot about keeping a little joey alive and Little Bill has been amazing. We even started a 'Save the Wildlife' campaign and that's been fun. But I've got to be careful that I don't sound like I'm getting to like Little Bill!

Feral Frenzy

Well, Mum is still trying to work out how to do her thing on Overflow Station and I guess we've all still got a lot to learn. But who would have thought that feral pigs would get into her precious veggie garden? I thought it was pretty exciting at the time. Mum, not so much!

Horse Play

Little Bill's insisted on turning me into a country boy since day one, and she reckoned that meant I had to learn to ride a horse. How hard can that be? I thought. Then she turned up on her humungous bay horse and I began to wonder… I felt a bit better when she said she'd get a small pony for me to learn on, until I saw the tiny, mean-looking Shetland pony she'd picked. Just getting onto it was hard enough, but in the end, that pony and I saved the day!

Exploding Dunny

There was a new cook at The Overflow when the shearers came back after the rain. It seems that the only thing shearers really care about is food. They know all the cooks between here and Broken Hill at least. And they seemed to already know about this new cook's curries - and not in a good way! Anyway, Little Bill and me got to be rouseabouts, and Big Bill gave me the really important job of cleaning the shearers' dunny as well. And when the explosion happened, no-one could pin it on me.

CPSIA information can be obtained
at www.ICGtesting.com
Printed in the USA
BVHW070748280922
648086BV00030B/1258